The Little C.H.A.M.P.S.™
Child Heroes Attached to Military Personnel

By Jennifer Fink and Debbie Fink, M.A.
Illustrated by Walter Blackwell

Published by Harmony Hearth,® LLC
HarmonyHearth.com

To the children who serve our country as their parents defend our freedoms. Go Champs!
Special thanks to the USO, the organization that led the way in helping this book see the light of day. *(JF and DF)*

Throughout our nation's history, millions of children have grown up in strong, grounded military families.
It is our hope that these five children serve as testaments to all those children: past, present, and future.
May God bless our troops and families. *(WB)*

To our families and friends who supported our efforts through their love and patience; and to the individuals and organizations that helped make this project a reality. It has been a team effort.

With an attitude of gratitude,

Jen, Debbie, and Walt

Published by

HARMONY HEARTH,® LLC
HarmonyHearth.com

Bethesda, MD
Printed in the U.S.A.
ISBN 978-0-9678871-5-9
HarmonyHearth.com

Book design by Caroline Smith Heming

A NOTE TO ADULTS

This book serves as a Public Health and Education Initiative with a dual purpose: 1) to provide Champs with coping tools to help them face their respective challenges, while celebrating their service to our country; and 2) to raise awareness among civilian children about the lives of their military-connected peers. This initiative aims to build a bridge of understanding between the civilian and military worlds by fostering an attitude of gratitude for our stoic Champs and their military families. To read the book with:

Military Children (Champs)
Take time to read the book over several sittings. If the Champ wants to talk about a topic elicited by the story, let him or her talk about it. Engage in the discussion. If the Champ wants to listen in silence, then respect that. Let the Champ know that any topic can be revisited at another time.

Champs often experience loss of normalcy when dealing with a deployed, deployable, injured, or wounded parent. Coping with any form of this loss has many stages, including: Shock; Denial; Fear/Depression; Anger; Regression; Bargaining; and Acceptance.*

Every person's experience is different. There is no formula for the order, duration, or number of stages experienced. Hence, each stage is imbedded in this story, opening the door for dialogue with the Champ.

Shock...................................Gonzo, p. 18
Denial..................................Smiley, p. 20
Fear/Depression..........Lo, p. 19; Smiley, pp. 19-21

Anger.....................Gonzo, p. 18; Smiley, p. 20
Regression.........Smiley, p. 20
Bargaining.......Lo, p. 19; Oboe, p. 22
Acceptance.......The Little Champs, pp. 46 – End

Civilian Children
Take time to read the book over several sittings. Make sure to read the definitions of the military lingo. If a child has questions, do your best to answer. After reading, seek out opportunities to connect with military families. For more information and volunteer opportunities, visit the USO website (USO.org), or find an organization that helps military families in your community. Most importantly, remember: Champs are fun loving kids, too!

For more information, activities, and ideas, visit TheLittleChamps.org

---

* Stages of loss were adapted for children by Debbie Fink, M.A., from the key work of Kubler-Ross, E. (2005).

PART ONE

Meet the Little Champs

Looking back, I was convinced that we were unstoppable. We were the best—and only—Capture the Flag team on our military base. We are called the Little Champs, because CHAMP stands for Child Heroes Attached to Military Personnel. We sure like the way that sounds.

But even with our awesome team, life as a Champ can be pretty unfair sometimes. We feel like people just don't get it.

Ever since the five of us found each other at the base's Youth Center, we became more than just teammates and friends—we became a family.

Here is some military lingo translated for our civilian friends:

Base — *a place used as the center of operations by the military; almost like a town. Many (but not all) military families live on a base. Army bases are called posts and all branches of the military also refer to bases as installations.*

Smiley

I am Samuel Smith III, co-captain of the Little Champs. During our games, it's my job to call the plays, and to make sure everyone plays by the rules. My teammates nicknamed me *Smiley* because I smile even when I'm sad or worried or scared or crying. Not that I cry . . . much . . . in public, anyway.

We PCSed to this base two years ago. My dad is a Commander in the United States Navy which makes me a Navy Champ. My mom volunteers for the USO when she's not working at her job or taking care of me. Lots of our family members serve in the Navy, and I plan to follow in their footsteps when I'm old enough.

My parents are really busy, but thankfully Dad finds time to toss a ball around with me. Football Sundays are the ultimate family event; my twin sisters still enjoy them when they come home from college. No matter where we are in the world, we don't miss a game.

Physical education (PE) and math are my favorite classes in school, and for fun I like to compare baseball players' stats. Enough about me—now it's time to introduce our team's other Champs . . .

PCS — *Permanent Change of Station; when a family is moved to a different base.*

Commander — *a senior officer rank in the Navy or Coast Guard.*

Navy — *founded on October 13, 1775.*

USO — *the United Service Organizations; a nonprofit organization with a mission to lift the spirits of America's troops and their families.*

Gonzo

Meet Tyler Gonzales. We call him *Gonzo.* Gonzo is our Most Valuable Player (MVP), and has captured the flag more than the rest of us combined. He just had a super fun birthday party, and boy was his homemade cake yummy!

Gonzo's an Army Champ (sometimes called an Army Brat). His dad, Staff Sergeant (SSG) Gonzales, might be the biggest man I've ever seen. Gonzo looks tiny when standing next to him. SSG Gonzales is the definition of "Hooah," as they say in the Army.

Army — *founded on June 14, 1775.*

Brat — *term some military families use for a child of a Servicemember. The title 'Brat' is worn by many with pride, from generation to generation. Originally, Brat stood for* **B***ritish* **R***egiment* **A***ttached* **T***raveler.*

"Hooah" — *the Army's enthusiastic reply. Some say it comes from "***H***eard-***U***nderstood-***A***cknowledged" (HUA).*

Gonzo's head is filled with facts. He watches history shows on TV, and reads about presidents and countries. Just yesterday Gonzo told me that Kaieteur is the tallest waterfall in Guyana. Until then I didn't even know Guyana was a country! Gonzo remembers history dates like I remember baseball stats. He doesn't like math much, so I help Gonzo with math and he's my go-to guy for history and social studies.

Gonzo is really protective of his little sister and brothers. When he gets too protective, Mrs. Gonzales quickly reminds him that the little ones already have parents to raise them. I think it's awesome that everyone in Gonzo's family speaks more than one language.

Then there's co-captain Angel Jones. We nicknamed her *Halo* and *nick*-nicknamed her *Lo*. Lo's dad, Gunnery Sergeant (*Gunny*) Jones is a Marine in the Marine Corps, which makes Lo a Marine Champ. I can feel the "Oorah" whenever her dad rolls into the room.

Lo is an awesome artist and an unbelievable gymnast. She is by far our best flag defender, although it's hard to keep her right-side-up in our games. Lo likes to walk around the base on her hands. When she's not upside down, she's usually drawing.

Marine Corps — *founded on November 10, 1775. "Corps" is pronounced "core."*

"Oorah" — *the Marine Corps' enthusiastic reply or verbal greeting.*

Lo's favorite class is art. She's also really good at English, because she loves to read and write. Lo writes poems for fun. I don't see how that's any fun at all. Lo also keeps a journal. She says it helps her deal with her feelings. For our birthdays, she gave us each a journal. She keeps asking if we're writing in them. That's so Lo.

When Lo grows up, she wants to be a professional poet, writer, and illustrator. I don't know if that'll be before, during, or after she competes in the Olympics!

Lo is an only child and is so much like her parents. Her dad can make anyone laugh, and her mom says the nicest things about everyone. Lo got the best of both of them . . . even if her jokes aren't always very funny.

Oboe

Next in line is Kenny Nez. Kenny's nickname is *Oboe* because he lives and breathes music (an oboe is a musical instrument). Oboe wrote our team theme song which we sing —after the national anthem—before every game . . . and I mean *every*.

Each time the national anthem is played at the base's movie theater, Oboe is first to jump up on his feet, put his hand over his heart, and sing.

Almost anything anybody says reminds Oboe of a song. Sometimes it's annoying, but his music always makes everybody smile. Oboe is definitely our team spirit.

Oboe is an Air Force Champ since his mom serves as a Major in the Air Force. We love listening to cool stories about the Nez family history. They've served in almost every branch of the military. Oboe's great-grandpa served in the Marine Corps as a Navajo Code Talker; his grandpa served in the Army; his uncle serves in the Coast Guard; his great-aunt serves in the National Guard; and his mom serves in the Air Force. Hopefully, Oboe will join the Navy, so we can serve together when we grow up.

Oboe's favorite subjects in school are music and science. He complains that he has to choose between orchestra and band. He wishes he could take both, especially if one could be instead of math. Oboe's family loves hiking and outdoor adventures. Their outings sure sound like a lot of fun.

Air Force — *founded on September 18, 1947.*

Navajo Code Talkers — *Native American Marines during WWII who sent secret messages over radios and phones in the Navajo language so the enemies wouldn't understand. They were key to the success of U.S. military operations during this war.*

National Guard — *founded on December 13, 1636. Citizens serving in the National Guard are called Citizen Servicemembers, and they have regular jobs in their communities.*

Soupy

Last but not least is Chrissy Campbell. We call her *Soupy*, even though she insists her family isn't related to *the* Campbell Soup family. Soupy is definitely a Coast Guard Champ. Her mom, Senior Chief Petty Officer (SCPO) Campbell, serves in the Coast Guard, and her stepbrother is in the Coast Guard Reserve.

Soupy is super fast and the quickest at tagging our opponents. My sisters tease me and say I have a crush on her, but that's just crazy talk. Double crazy, in their case!

Coast Guard — *founded on August 4, 1790.*

Reserve — *trained units and qualified persons that help their active duty forces. Each service branch has a Reserve Command.*

Soupy likes almost every subject in school. She always works hard, and it sure pays off when report cards come around. The teachers love Soupy—and she can talk her way out of any situation.

There have been plenty of times when she's come to the rescue of one of us. Once I got in trouble for some silly reason with the science teacher. Soupy defended me and before I knew it, everything was back to normal, and the teacher was even laughing! I don't know how Soupy does it. She sure should become a lawyer.

PART TWO

Champ Challenges

Moving Facts* — *Champs move an average of 6-9 times between Kindergarten and 12th grade, and attend an average of at least 6-9 schools in that time.*

* *Statistics from Military Child Education Coalition, 2011.*

So that's the Little Champs family: me; Gonzo; Lo; Oboe; and Soupy. Once, for fun, we did the math for the total number of moves we've made in our lives:

MOVING FACTS

Me:	7
+	
Oboe:	6
+	
Soupy:	5
+	
Gonzo:	4
+	
Lo:	3
- - - - - - - -	

25 moves in total

As military Champs, every few years our families are packing up, picking up, and moving again.

We sure can move on the field, too. We capture a flag like no other!

The five of us arrived on the base at different times. Between the Youth Center and American Red Cross SAF events, we became fast friends. We play, laugh, study, dream, and (try to) stay out of trouble together. We depend on one another.

Each of us knows what it feels like to be really lonely, so we're super grateful that we found each other. Even though our situations are different, it's great to have friends who understand military life.

With such special friendships, how can things be so hard? Life on base was fine until things started to unravel like a ball of yarn . . .

American Red Cross SAF — *American Red Cross **S**ervice to the **A**rmed **F**orces; a nonprofit organization that supports and provides assistance to military families worldwide.*

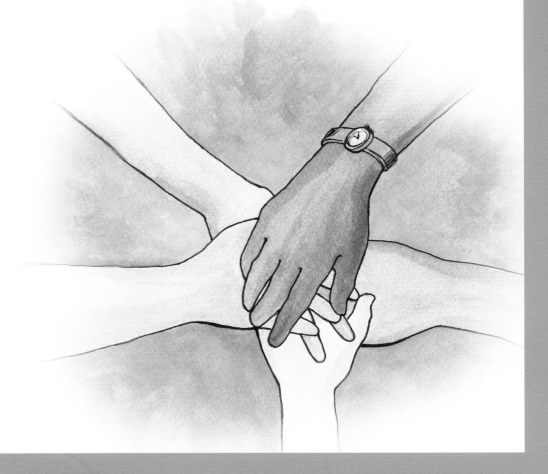

It all started to fall apart when Gonzo heard that his dad was scheduled to deploy again. This would be SSG Gonzales' third tour in a war zone. Gonzo couldn't—*wouldn't*—believe his ears.

Dealing with deployments isn't new for us Champs, but still, that does not make them any easier. Our parents' deployments can be depressing, scary, or sad—no matter how many times we go through them. As many of us say, "Gone is gone."

Ever since Gonzo got over the initial shock, he's been really angry. I think a punching bag would help him, but it would probably take up too much of his bedroom in the military family housing. It's upsetting to see Gonzo so angry; yet my mom reminds me, "We all deal with the stress of deployment differently."

Deploy — *when a Servicemember gets sent overseas for a period of time without his/her family; usually to fight in a war.*

Tour — *to go "on tour" is another way of saying "to go on assignment."*

Military family housing — *family homes on a military base.*

Gone is gone — *a phrase used by Champs when a parent is deployed. While it means s/he is gone for now, it does not mean s/he is gone forever.*

The next blow came when Lo's dad, Gunny, heard that he was being medically retired. Injured in combat, Gunny Jones is called a Wounded Warrior. He was awarded a Purple Heart.

When Gunny first came back injured, Lo was scared. Seeing his injuries scared me, too. I couldn't help thinking, "If it happened to *her* dad, could it happen to mine?"

Lo's mom explained that feeling scared was normal, and it would pass with time and talking about it. I wondered how much time and talking it would take.

Why do so many people talk about Wounded Warriors without talking about their families? Lo hurts, too, but she keeps smiling, spinning, and drawing. I think Lo thinks that if she acts cheery and works hard, then her dad will recover faster. I dunno. Maybe he will. Maybe he won't. I *hope* he will.

But Gunny's injury hasn't stopped him. He smiles, pops wheelies, and still makes Lo laugh. Gunny loves sports and plans to train for the Warrior Games.

Since Gunny's injury, he has been going through the long process to get medically retired so they can move back to California to live near family. The time has finally come.

I feel selfish saying this, but what about our Little Champs' family?

Medical retirement/medical discharge — *when a Servicemember is honorably discharged from the military after being injured or wounded.*

Wounded Warriors — *Servicemembers who have been injured or wounded while serving.*

Purple Heart — *military medal given to Servicemembers wounded in action.*

Warrior Games — *athletic competitions for wounded, ill, and injured Servicemembers and Veterans.*

Just when I thought the situation couldn't get any worse . . . it did. My dad, dressed in his civies, came to tuck me in last night. He told me he was taking a job on the East Coast. I was sure I heard him wrong. Or maybe it was a nightmare.

Dad's been stationed at this base for what feels like a long time, so I figured we would move sometime soon. But I never thought the day would come *this* soon. I just don't understand how he can take me away from my friends—again!

I felt like the earth was pulled out from under my bed and I was freefalling.

Dad shut my door behind him. I curled into a tight ball and cried myself to sleep. I was embarrassed when I had to change my bed sheets the next morning.

Civies — *civilian clothing, or any clothing that is not a military uniform. Also spelled 'civvies.'*

After breakfast, I met the team. Given all our news, we sure didn't feel like playing. I tried smiling, holding back tears that could've filled an ocean. We sat and complained—except Oboe who acted like none of this was happening.

I fought my tears back and said, "We need to do something to hold us together when we feel like we're falling apart."

"Like what?" grumbled Gonzo angrily.

Lo piped up, "Like, when Dad deployed, he told me to look up at the moon before I got into bed. He'd be looking at the moon, too, so we'd feel connected. It helped."

"Or we could just video chat 24/7," mumbled Gonzo.

"No. I need something I can see and touch to remember all our good times, no matter what different time zones we're in," said Soupy.

"Let's think," I said, and think and think and think and think we did.

PART THREE
Operation Champ Chests

"Got it!" Lo shouted, as she shot up in the air. "Let's make Champ Chests! We'll each find our own container to use as our chest. Then we'll collect special things to put in *each other's* chests. We'll keep our Champ Chests with us from move to move. That way we'll all be together, no matter where we are in the world."

"Maybe if we make these chests, everything will stay just the way it is," hoped Oboe aloud.

"No, it won't, Oboe," charged Lo. "Change is gonna' happen whether we're ready or not. Just deal with it— let's try to thrive, not just survive."

Lo's words poured over us like a bucket of ice-cold, salty seawater. Oboe locked eyes with Lo, nodded, then turned to face us. Leave it to Lo to knock us to our senses.

"So who's in with Lo's chest challenge? Who wants to search for a container?" Soupy asked excitedly.

"I'm in," I said. "This might be the first time that I haven't just packed my bags and moved on."

"Roger that! Well, what are we waiting for?" piped in Oboe.

My heart felt a bit lighter thanks to Lo. I think all our hearts hurt a little less once we took control and moved into action.

Lo looked at her watch and announced, "We have T-minus **30** minutes to find our chests. The time now is 1421. We'll meet back on the playground at 1451."

Together we shouted,

"READY? SET? GO!"

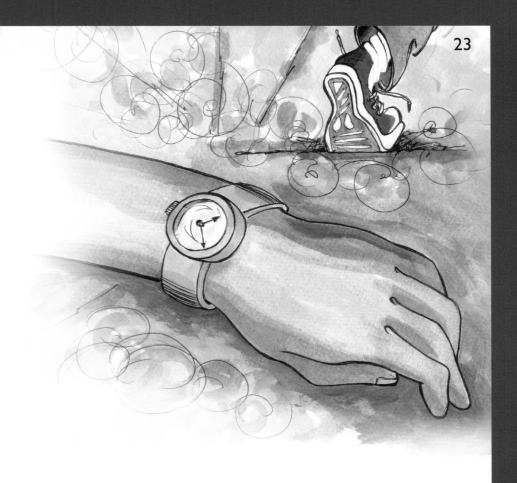

Roger that — an aviation code word meaning "I received and understood your entire message."

T-minus — time (T), minus whatever amount of time is left until an event happens; used by both the military and National Aeronautics and Space Administration (NASA).

1421 — military time is on a 24 hour clock instead of 12, meaning 1421 is military time for 2:21 p.m. civilian time.

1451 — do the math!

Oboe darted directly down to the band's practice room. Just last week, while helping the bandleader Capt McKinley clean up, Oboe had seen a broken clarinet case behind the Captain's desk.

Oboe grabbed the loose handle and searched for Capt McKinley.

"Capt McKinley, are you still using your old case, or may I please have it?" Oboe asked.

"It's all yours, Oboe. I don't know why you want it, but go right ahead. I've had that case since high school. Reduce, Reuse, Recycle!"

Oboe thanked Capt McKinley, and raced back to the playground, excitedly inspecting his soon-to-be Champ Chest as he waited for his friends.

Capt — *Air Force notation for Captain. All branches have Captains, but it can mean different ranks in each branch.*

Soupy sprinted straight to the mess hall.

"Miss Martha!" Soupy sputtered, "do you have any empty, super-sized soup cans?"

"You bet, Miss Soupy," said Miss Martha, "I was just about to toss them. There's tomato and chicken noodle. Take your pick, and I'll smooth out the sharp edges so you don't get hurt. Not that I know what you'll be doing with it."

Soupy smiled, swooped up the smoothed-out tomato soup can, thanked Miss Martha, and scooted off to the swings.

Mess hall — *dining facility or cafeteria.*

I scratched my head thinking about what to use. It finally came to me—my first toolbox would be perfect! It holds a good amount, and its lock and key still work.

I hurried home, and found my old tool chest just where I had stored it. With the toolbox tucked tightly under my arm, I sprinted back to the slide.

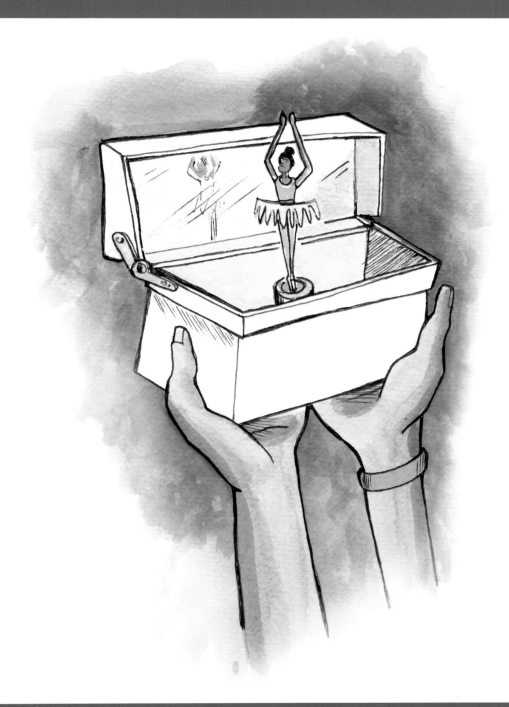

Lo cartwheeled all the way home —her head spinning with ideas. Her pencil pouch? Too small. Her doll case? Too big. Her lunch box? Too needed. Her jewelry box? Just right! Gunny had bought it for her birthday, and in it a ballerina twirled to her favorite lullaby.

Holding her jewelry box with two hands, Lo cautiously walked back to meet the Champs near the monkey bars.

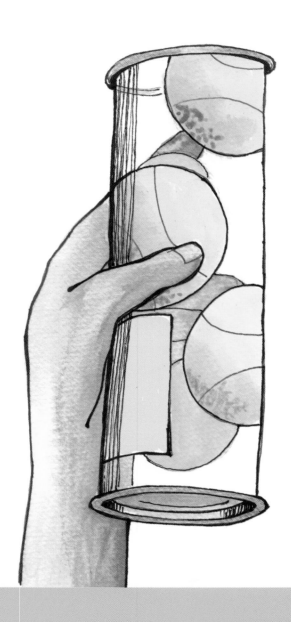

Gonzo headed home. Right outside the front door, he bumped into his mom, who was carrying bags back from the commissary.

Mrs. Gonzales said, "Hey, bud, would you please help me with the groceries? Thanks."

"Um, I'm kinda . . ." Gonzo said before his mom stated, "No 'kinda', kiddo. It'll take you all of ten minutes."

"Sure," grumbled Gonzo. After the food was put away, Gonzo—who is easily sidetracked—sat down to eat a snack. Mid-bite, he looked at the clock and yelped, "Oh nooooo, I'm gonna' be late!"

He scanned the space in search of a chest and zoomed in on a tennis ball tube. It had one ball in it. "One ball sure didn't need a whole container," thought Gonzo.

Gonzo shook the container empty and flew out the door. He showed up late—but better late than never!

Commissary — *where military personnel and families shop for groceries.*

Back at the playground, we *ooh*ed and *aah*ed and *hooah*ed and *oorah*ed over each other's chests.

"Now that we have our chests, what do we put in them?" I asked.

"I think we should each find five mini-flags of our family's military branch. And if we can't find 'em . . . make 'em," exclaimed Oboe.

"Can we work on the flags together?" asked Gonzo, almost grumble-free. We all knew Gonzo relied on Soupy for anything creative.

Soupy picked up on Gonzo's hint. She giggled and said, "I'll work with you. Except first, you have to smile. Second, don't blame me if your Army flags end up looking a lot like Coast Guard flags!"

Everyone laughed. Even Gonzo.

PART FOUR

capture the Flags

This task was a piece of cake for me. With one request to my mom (who collects the flags given away at the annual Navy Ball), I had five perfectly pre-made mini Navy flags instantly.

Feeling guilty that this activity was so easy, I roamed from one Champ to the next to see if I could help.

Oboe happily worked alone. He poured himself a tall glass of lemonade and parked himself at the computer. With just a little help from his mom, Oboe found the perfect Air Force flag on the internet. He printed five copies and trimmed them with his left-handed scissors.

"What," thought Oboe, "can I use for flag poles?"

He slurped his lemonade, gulped, and yelped, "Aha!" Oboe dug through the kitchen pantry and found the box of straws. He chose five and taped a straw to each flag.

Oboe then rolled each flag, and used his much-hated orthodontic rubber bands to hold the flags in place.

"Finally," muttered Oboe, "these bands are good for something." Looking at his flags, Oboe smiled.

Gonzo and Soupy set their plan into action. Soupy sent Gonzo to find five straight and sturdy somethings that he could use as flag holders.

While Gonzo searched for his sticks, Soupy printed and cut out his five Army flags and her five Coast Guard flags.

Just as Soupy finished all ten flags, Gonzo returned. Smiling, he held out his five twigs ("not so straight," thought Soupy, "but they were sturdy and would do the job").

Soupy then left Gonzo with a roll of tape to attach his flags to the twigs. Her parting words were, "Whatever you do, Gonzo, don't mess up. I'm not making any more Army flags!" They both laughed.

Soupy went to find a box of glow-in-the-dark sticks she had been saving. Now was the perfect time to use them.

Lo sprawled out with her colored pencils, a ruler, and a compass. While she drew her five Marine flags, she thought about what would work as a stick. Lo being Lo, the flags had to be perfect. Fun. Different.

A pretzel stick? Too crumbly. A piece of licorice? Too limpy. A knitting needle? Too sharp. A candy stick? Just right! Lo found her candy sticks and chose a different color for each of her teammates' flags.

The next time our team met, we showed off our flags. I was a bit embarrassed that mine were not homemade. We then placed one of our flags in each of the five Champ Chests.

"Are we done?" asked Gonzo.

"Nope! Now comes the tough stuff. We need to find an item that represents who we are," declared Soupy.

"How the heck are we gonna' do that?" asked Gonzo.

"I don't know yet," Soupy said, sounding discouraged.

Lo suggested, "What if we each ask an adult what two things make us special? Maybe that'll lead us to our mystery item. It'll be like a detective game where we're solving our own mystery."

Everyone agreed to give it a go.

Lo then pushed, "Next meeting? O'dark-thirty."

"No way," I complained. "I'll still be sleeping."

"Okay, then," said Lo, "Tomorrow—same time, same place."

O'dark-thirty — *an early morning report time.*

JOY

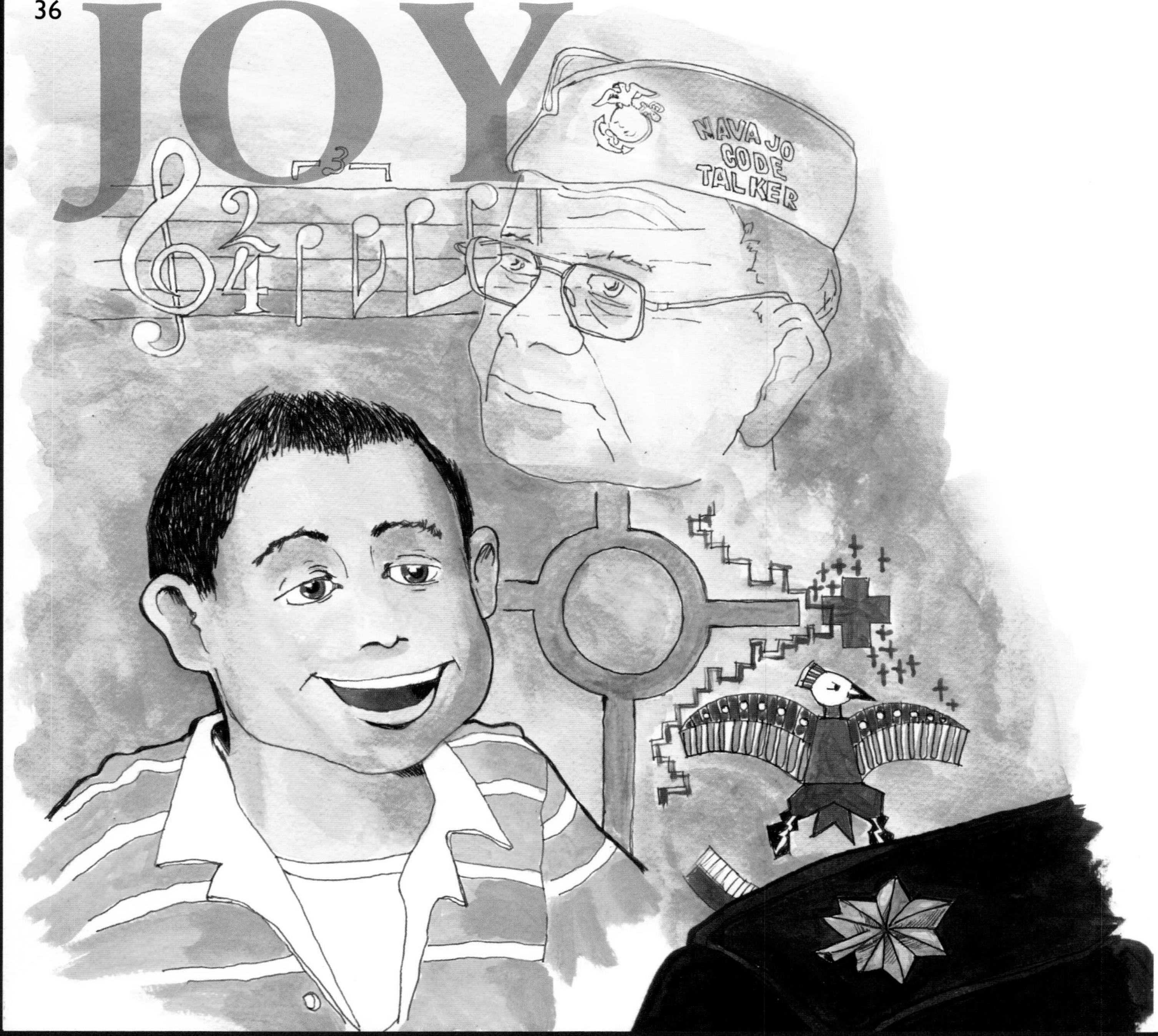

UNITY

PART FIVE

Mission I Am Me

"Hey mom, what two things are special about me?" asked Oboe.

Mom responded, "Where do I begin? Hmmm . . . I would say your love for music, stemming from your Navajo roots brings JOY and UNITY to those with whom you share your gift. Joy and unity are both virtues."

"Joy?" Oboe asked.

"Yes," his mom explained. "Joy gets us through our toughest times, and it softens sad feelings."

"Unity?" he asked again.

"Absolutely," Oboe's mom continued, "Unity connects one person to another and connects all living things. Music creates unity.

"Another example of unity is our family's service to our country. Your great-grandfather served in a way only Native Americans could. Your grandfather, uncle, great-aunt, and I have also served our nation proudly.

"But to sum *you* up, Oboe, it's the joy and unity you express through your music," his mother finished.

"Mom, how can I fit that into a container?" Oboe asked.

"I leave that up to you," Oboe's mom said in her singsong voice.

TRUST

"Dad, what makes me *me*?" stammered Gonzo.

"Excuse me? What makes you *you* is us," Dad said. "I don't know why you're asking, but I suppose what makes you *you* is your sense of direction in life. Your PATIENCE and your TRUST."

"What do you mean?" Gonzo pushed.

SSG Gonzales explained, "Your patience is a commitment to what lies ahead. It's the acceptance of the present while you wait for the future. It is the hope inside of you that everything will be okay.

"Your trust is key. Even when life gets really hard—and we know it will get harder when I'm deployed—it is trust that helps us dig deep and get through even the toughest situations.

"With my deployment getting closer—and yes, I know that's why you're so angry these days—both your patience and trust will be put to the test."

"Oh," Gonzo responded quietly, thinking about what his dad said, and surprised he knew why Gonzo has been so angry.

Dad went on, "What makes you *you* is your internal compass. Listen to it. Trust it—even when you get sidetracked."

"What can I find to stand for all that heavy stuff?" Gonzo asked.

"Patience, bud. I trust that you will find the perfect item," Gonzo's dad finished.

PATIENCE

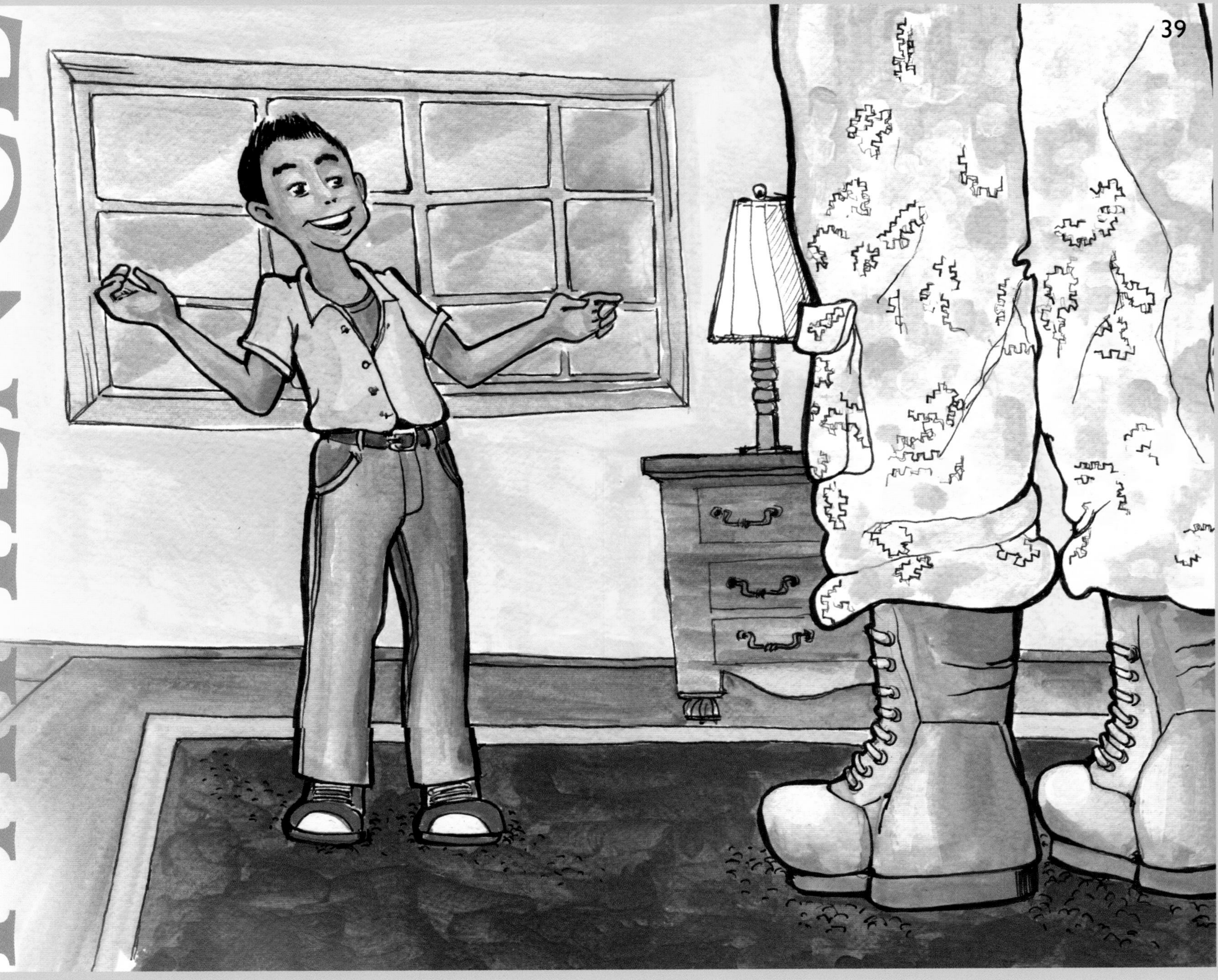

"Mom, describe me in TWO words!" blurted Soupy.

Soupy's mom exclaimed: "In only two words? Why?"

"The Little Champs are doing a project to help us go our separate ways," Soupy explained.

SCPO Campbell continued, "That's so meaningful! Well, aside from amazing, brilliant, compassionate . . ."

Soupy said, "Okay, Mom, I get it. Seriously. Two of my best qualities would be . . .?"

After a long pause, Soupy's mom said, "ASSERTIVENESS and FORGIVENESS."

"Why?" asked Soupy.

Soupy's mom began, "For starters, you work so hard in school. You've had to enter many new schools, feeling at first like you don't belong, time after time.

"Your assertiveness pushes you to work hard, to make new friends, and to give the world the best you've got. You know what you stand for, and stand for what you know.

"As for forgiveness, we should all strive to be as forgiving as you. With your dad and me divorced, you find forgiveness in your heart—even when he forgets your birthday. Yet remember, not *all* actions are forgivable," finished SCPO Campbell.

"I know, Mom. You've explained that over and over. So what would be a good object to symbolize assertiveness and forgiveness?" asked Soupy.

Her mom warmly responded, "That, my dear, I leave entirely up to you."

FORGIVENESS

ASSERTIVENESS

"Mom? Dad? I have a question," I said.

"Sweety, we're getting ready for tonight's Dining Out. Can it wait until later?" Mom asked.

I completely forgot that tonight was their big night out. I didn't want to bother them.

"Yeah, no problem," I said. "Can I go ask Kevin instead?" I responded.

"If you make it quick and are home before we leave," agreed Dad.

"Okay!" I yelled, as I slid out the door to find my cousin, who works as a gate guard.

"Kevin, what makes me special?" I asked.

"Now that's not a question I hear very often." After some silence, Kevin said, "Well, I'd say it's your COMMITMENT and GRATITUDE."

COMMITMENT

"What do you mean?" I questioned.

Kevin answered, "Commitment is when you care deeply about something or someone and stay loyal no matter what. I see your commitment to your team at your games. You're a committed friend, son, brother, cousin, student, and citizen. You are the glue among many."

"If you say so . . . Why gratitude?" I pushed.

"Gratitude," explained Kevin, "is being grateful for what we have. It means having a grateful heart. You have an attitude of gratitude for those you love and for the world you live in."

"Wow. Thanks, Kevin." I let his words sink in. Eventually I asked, "So if you needed an item that stood for those things, what would you choose?"

Kevin said smiling, "I sure don't know, but can't wait to find out."

Dining Out — a special event for officers and their spouses that dates back to the days of George Washington.

Gate guard — a guard who stands watch and checks identification papers at the main entrance to the base or post.

"Daddy!" called Lo.

"Yes, Angel?"

"What two things make me one-of-a-kind?" asked Lo.

"What doesn't? There's a reason we named you Angel."

Lo's dad then said seriously, "When I got injured, it brought out the best and worst in everyone. Your PERSEVERANCE and FLEXIBILITY have been most admirable.

"So much has changed since my injury, and more will change with my medical discharge. Your perseverance—which means pushing through and not giving up—has been crucial. Your flexibility—which means your openness to change—is something we rely on. With change comes growth. You, my Angel, exemplify that."

Lo thought back to the days when she'd been scared. It felt like forever ago. Talking, drawing, and writing about her feelings had helped her work through her fears.

"Okay, so sum that up in two words, please," begged Lo.

Dad responded, "Perseverance and flexibility."

"What would symbolize these virtues?" she pushed.

"*You!*" Lo's dad exclaimed.

"Some help you are, Daddy." Lo giggled.

Detective Lo thought long and hard, and eventually she solved her mystery. Lo couldn't wait until the team's next meeting where she'd get to show and tell—and give.

Tomorrow felt like an eternity away.

PERSEVERANCE

FLEXIBILITY

PART SIX

Goodbyes Are Not Forever

Lo could hardly contain herself when the Little Champs met. She blurted out, "I've got to go first—or I'm just gonna' burst!"

Lo continued, "Okay, here it goes. Drum roll . . . my item is . . . stretchy putty!" Lo tossed an egg-shaped container into each of our laps.

"Here's why. What makes me one-of-a-kind is my PERSEVERANCE and FLEXIBILITY. Just like this putty, when we persevere, we stretch our limits and we can always stretch a little more.

"Also, just like stretchy putty, we need to be flexible and open to change. So, with this putty, I want you to remember my gymnastics tricks; and more importantly, take some of my perseverance and flexibility with you wherever you go."

We cheered. In a blink of an eye, Lo stood on her hands, popped back to her feet, bowed, and smiled. She then added with a huge grin, "Always remember to look at life from different angles. It sure helps to see things from a new perspective!"

Oboe stood up next and immediately started us singing our team song. Then he began:

"The two virtues—to use my mom's big word—that make me special are JOY and UNITY. Through my music I bring joy and unity. Joy helps get us through the toughest times, like right now, and softens our sadness. Unity connects people to each other and all living things . . . like how we're united as Champs, no matter where we are in the world.

"So I made us our very own Little Champs' songbook with seven songs: the national anthem, the song for each military branch, and our Little Champs' song!"

Oboe hummed our team song while he handed each of us our super special songbook.

Gonzo grinned as he got up. He pulled out five small compasses from a paper bag. "Yes," Gonzo explained, "my item is a compass."

Continuing, he said: "My dad thinks that what makes me *me* is my PATIENCE and TRUST. My patience is the hope inside that everything will turn out okay. I trust that everything will be all right even when life gets hard.

"Dad told me I should follow my internal compass. While I do get distracted, he says I have a strong sense of direction in life.

"With this compass, never lose sight of where you're going; never forget where you've been; and always take time to explore where you are!

"As you all know, I've been really angry lately. Thank you for sticking by me."

Soupy spoke up. "My object is a pencil!"

"Why?" Soupy continued, "Because Mom said ASSERTIVENESS and FORGIVENESS were my qualities. The pencil point is for assertiveness. We must assert ourselves in school and elsewhere. Let's give the world the best we've got. Each time we enter a new school or situation, we have to bring our courage, confidence, and positive attitude.

"The eraser stands for forgiveness. We need to find it in our hearts to forgive. When we forgive someone, it's like we erase some of what happened.

"Still, Mom points out that sometimes bad things happen that are *not* erasable. In these situations, Mom says, find and tell a trusted adult. If that adult doesn't listen or help, find a trusted adult who *does* listen and help.

"So whether you're in school or just holding a pencil, think of me. You know I'd be telling you to try your hardest. And never forget to forgive."

There was a mixture of moans and giggles among us.

Last but not least, I pulled out my brown bag.

"Glue sticks!" I shouted. "My cousin says my COMMITMENT and GRATITUDE make me special.

"Commitment is when we care deeply about something and *stick by* no matter what. Get it?"

I was on a roll. A sticky roll.

"Gratitude is when we're grateful for what we have. Our attitude of gratitude has to *stick* to us like our shadow. Gratitude helps us focus on the positive, even in hard times—like now. For example, I am grateful for our friendships."

I continued, "Our Champ Chests capture our special memories and lots of virtues that'll stick with us through life. With our five flags, Lo's stretchy putty, Oboe's songbook, Gonzo's compass, Soupy's pencil, and my glue stick, we are GTG!

"Remember that it's never 'Goodbye,' but . . ."

GTG — *good to go.*

We all cheered together,

"SEE YOU LATER!"

Lo called out, "Group hug!"
For one last time our team huddled,
and sang the lyrics from our song:

Goodbyes are not forever,
Goodbyes are not the end,
They simply mean we'll miss you,
Until we meet again!*

---

* *Lyrics written by an unknown author.*

PART SEVEN

New Beginnings

After our final huddle, we pushed our Champ Chests under a tree and raced toward the field to play one last game of Capture the Flag.

Finally accepting the coming changes, we hoped other kids would step up to play. As if out of nowhere, three new Champs appeared on the field.

"Hey, can we play?" asked one of the new kids, her face covered with freckles. I thought to myself, "She has the nickname *Freckles* written all over her."

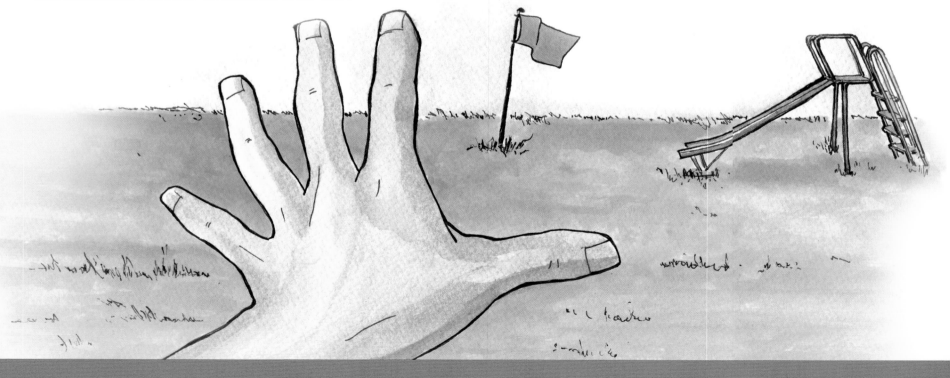

"Absolutely!" Gonzo shouted excitedly.

As we all scrambled to start our game, it was then that I realized: these were new beginnings for all of us. Our team would survive. While some players were moving on, new players were moving in. They'd have to learn our team song, and they'd need to sing the national anthem before every game. Then, and only then, could we pass the flag on to the new Little Champs.

I have since moved, braved my first day in school, and scouted out kids to form a Capture the Flag team.

What have I learned? I've learned that life as a Champ comes with both challenges and benefits. It's what makes me *me!* I live in many exciting places and experience lots of cultures; I make new friends, scattered all over the world; and, because of Dad's service, I am proud to say my family helps keep America safe and strong.

So life really isn't so unfair after all. It's just, as Lo would say, "how we choose to look at it."

As we say in the Navy, "Fair winds and following seas."

No matter where we're headed, this is a way to wish smooth sailing to all . . .

. . . until we meet again.

Meet the Creators

Photo by Anthony Brice

JENNIFER FINK (middle)

Jen studies Public Health and Military Studies at the University of Maryland and is passionate about engaging the civilian community in giving back to military families. She has interned for the American Red Cross Service to the Armed Forces and for Operation Homefront, and received The President's Volunteer Service Award and the Red Cross Youth Volunteer of the Year Award at Walter Reed National Military Medical Center. Jen is Founder and CEO of the nonprofit organization Operation CHAMPS (*OperationChamps.org*).

DEBBIE FINK (left)

Debbie is an author, educator, and performer, whose books, workshops, and performances reach audiences globally. As a USO Tour Vet, Debbie has had the honor of 'edu-taining' over 10,000 Champs residing in Asia and Europe. She delivers messages of support, comfort, and gratitude to our Nation's Champs through Operation CHAMPS' public health and education initiative and Operation Thanksgiving Eagle. She also runs the Mom of Many Hats global health initiative, helping families cope with a cancer diagnosis (*MomOfManyHats.com*).

WALTER BLACKWELL (right)

Walter is a U.S. Navy Veteran and former President/CEO of the National Veterans Business Development Corporation (TVC). Career highlights include private industry, international business and nonprofit arenas. A graduate of Washington University, he has authored and illustrated children's books and one-man plays, and currently is launching a personal cloud platform start-up.